THE
BATE
COLLECTION

ANDREW LAMB

ISBN 978-0-9930442-0-5

10 9 8 7 6 5 4 3 2

Printed by
Printed by Dolman Scott Ltd
www.dolmanscott.co.uk

contents

INTRODUCTION

Welcome to the Bate Collection, in the Faculty of Music, University of Oxford, the most comprehensive collection of European woodwind, brass and percussion instruments in Britain. The Bate has over 2000 instruments from the Western orchestral music traditions from the Renaissance, through the Baroque, Classical, Romantic and up to modern times. More than a thousand instruments are on display, by the most important English, French and German makers and from pre-eminent collectors. In addition to instruments the Bate also hosts a selection of portraits from the Faculty of Music collection, a highlight of which is a large portrait of Georg Frederic Handel by T. Hudson.

The Bate Collection
in the Faculty of Music,
University of Oxford

The Collection takes its name from Philip Bate who gave his extensive collection of European woodwind instruments to the University of Oxford in 1968. The Bate is unique in that many of the instruments are played, this results from the original condition of gift, that students should have access to and be able to play these instruments. The Collection has grown, in large due to the dedication and support of both individuals and groups such as the Friends of the Bate Collection who have made several gifts. The Collection now houses the Reginald Morley-Pegge Collection of horns, brass and woodwind instruments; the Edgar Hunt Collection of Recorders; and the William Retford Memorial Collection of Bows along with other important collections.

The lower gallery with historic keyboard instruments.

woodwind

instruments

INTRODUCTION TO WOODWIND
MUSICAL INSTRUMENTS

Woodwind instruments can be divided into a number of sub-groups according to the means of playing them. They share the acoustical quality, along with brass instruments, of producing sound by the vibration of air molecules along the playing length of the instrument. The tonal quality can be varied according to the method of setting up the vibrations. The most familiar versions are:

• **Edge instruments**, or Flutes in which a narrow stream of air is directed against an edge to excite a column of air in a tube. Typical examples would include flutes, recorders and whistles.
• **Single reed instruments**, in which a column of air is made to vibrate by the intermittent access of an air stream produced by means of a reed. Examples of this would include clarinets and saxophones.
• **Double reed instruments**, in which a column of air is made to vibrate by the intermittent access of an air stream produced by means of two reeds vibrating against each other. Examples would include shawms, oboes and bassoons.

Many woodwind instruments have their origins in the ancient world and as a group they have undergone many developments over the past few hundred years. The diversity of these instruments in style, material, decoration and technical features such as number of keys, is due to both the period and the tendencies and tastes of particular makers in given geographical locations.

Probably the earliest known of man-made musical instrument was a type of whistle made of animal bone. Archaeologists have discovered examples that have been radio-carbon dated and found to be nearly 40,000 years old.

RECORDERS

The recorder is one of the most ancient woodwind instruments and has been played in this country since the Medieval period. The earliest surviving recorder in the world is thought to be a 14th century instrument currently located in Göttingen. Recorders normally have eight tone holes in all: seven on the front and one on the back. The recorder was immensely popular during the Renaissance and Baroque periods, but fell out of favour towards the end of the 17th century. The modern recorder is based on the Baroque version of the instrument, and only began to regain popularity in the early 20th century, initially as part of the revival of interest in early music.

FLUTE OR RECORDER?

Up until the 18th century the term 'flute' was used almost exclusively to refer to the recorder and sometimes more specifically to refer to the treble recorder.

Recorders are made in different sizes, with compasses corresponding to different vocal ranges. There are four main instruments in use today: the descant (lowest note c); treble (lowest note f), tenor (lowest note c) and bass (f). Sopranino (f) and great bass (c) instruments are also fairly common. The treble and tenor are used as non-transposing instruments, but music for the sopranino, descant, bass and great bass is customarily written an octave below their sounding pitch.

In the Renaissance period, recorders were frequently played in consorts. Instruments of various different sizes were used to produce dance music or to accompany voice. In this period, the recorder had a very wide, almost cylindrical bore, which made the instrument louder than its successors. The earliest recorder in the Collection is probably the 16th century Basset Recorder, which is most likely Italian in origin by the Bassano family. The Baroque period saw a number of changes to the way recorders were constructed: the bore (internal chamber) of the instrument was tapered, with the widest point at the mouthpiece. The Bate has several outstanding specimens from this period. Most notable, are the treble and Bb descant by Pierre Jaillard (known as 'Peter Bressan') who

FOCUS ON...

the Bressan Treble Recorder

This instrument was made in about 1720 by the celebrated baroque recorder maker Pierre Jaillard, also known as 'The Bressan'. He earned this soubriquet as he came from Bourg-en-Bresse, the capital of Ain province near Lyon in South-central France. At the age of 15, Jaillard was apprenticed to a local wood-turner but he left after two years. It is not known where he learned his instrument making skills but it is speculated that he studied in Paris along with his contemporary Rippert. He moved to England in 1688 and accompanied William III to the Netherlands as one of the King's 'Hautboys'.

This instrument came from the collection of Edgar Hunt. It had been kept in his flat in London which had been bombed during the blitz. Hunt returned to the site some days after the event and, whilst poking about in the rubble, was overjoyed to find the instrument wrapped up in an old shirt.

It is regarded as being one of the finest surviving instruments by the maker, and one of the least modified for instruments of the period.

A globally iconic instrument

this is one of the most famous recorders in the world and is used as a model for modern copies.

Historical recorders have been decorated using ivory. Nowadays this would be regarded as unacceptable.

the Bassano Basset recorder

Perhaps the oldest historical recorder in the Collection is the basset recorder. It is made of one piece of maple. The key is of brass with a double touch, which is probably a replacement. The spring is now an elastic band. Typical of the design of the period is a fontanelle that covers the key. The bottom of the foot has become damaged over time but this is to be expected with instruments of this age. There is an intriguing makers mark towards the top of the instrument that appears to resemble two double pairs of exclamation marks: !! !!. In fact, this closely matches the makers mark of the Bassano family, which was meant to be a moth. This instrument is representative of one of the family of renaissance instruments that were played in consort.

Our earliest recorder
The keywork is protected by a decorative fontanelle that is typical of Rennaissance design

arrived in London in 1688. He was employed by William III as one of the King's oboists and accompanied him to fight in Europe against Louise XIV of France. Bressan was the leading London recorder maker of his time and his recorders provide a model for recorder makers today. Included in the Collection is a bass recorder, which is similar in style to much of his work. Other notable instruments include the Tenor 4th flute by Stanesby Junior (who was active in the early 18th century).

FOCUS ON...

Thomas Stanesby Junior

The Bate Collection has the privilege of holding a number of instruments by one of the finest English baroque woodwind makers; Thomas Stanesby Junior. We have an oboe, a bass flute, a tenor 4th flute (recorder) and an ivory flute. The Stanesby family worked in London in the first half of the 18th century. Along with Bressan, the Stanesbys were responsible for most of the finest surviving English Baroque woodwind instruments. Thomas Stanesby Junior (bap. London, 25 Dec 1692; d Brompton (now London), 2 March 1754) was apprenticed to his father, Thomas Stanesby Senior, in 1706 and set up his own establishment over the Temple Exchange in Fleet Street near St Dunstan-in-the-West soon after being released from his indenture in 1713. In 1728 he received the Freedom of the Turners' Company; in 1739 he was elected master. In 1734 he inherited all his father's tools and a seal ring.

Stanesby's later instruments became simpler in exterior design when compared with the older Baroque style. It is thought that this was following the general trend toward the classical woodwind design. One typical example of this is the design of his oboe held in the Collection.

A new System of the FLUTE A'BEC. or Common ENGLISH FLUTE.

WHEREIN is propos'd to render that Instrument Universally usefull in Concert, without the trouble of Transposing the Musick for it. Humbly Dedicated to all those Gentlemen who like the Instrument.

By THO: STANESBY Jun.[r]

WHEREAS, it may be suppos'd, that the Projectors of the F. Flute commonly call'd the Concert Flute, never intended it for an Instrument to be us'd Universally in Concert, by their making it to go no lower than F. and as they made their Basses in F. also never intended other Basses to be us'd with them, than those of their own kind, by which a progression of one sort of Tone only is Effected; But we find now in all great Performances of Musick, that a mixture of Tones by different sorts of Instruments is best approv'd, and the Flute only is excluded, being incapable of Concerting with the rest, having a deficiency of three usefull Notes at the bottom; and though 'tis an easy Instrument, and the Compass extensive, yet for that deficiency can't Universally be us'd.

MANY great Masters, and delightfull Performers on this Instrument have endeavoured to make it acceptable in Concert by Composing the Flute part in one Key, when the other

18th century advertisement
extolling the virtues of Stanesby's designs

TRANSVERSE FLUTES

The transverse flute did not really gain in popularity until the Baroque period, although before this it was sometimes used in consort along with the recorder and the viol. In this period, the flute was redesigned:

the bore of the instrument was tapered towards the foot joint, which increased its range and, from the 1720s onwards, the flute began to be made in four separate pieces. By the early 18th century the flute had gained respect as a solo instrument, with composers such as Bach, Telemann and Vivaldi, creating solo pieces for them. The oldest in the Collection belong to this phase. A flute by the important Parisian maker, Thomas Lot (1708-1787) has four corps de rechange (middle sections allowing the instrument to be played at different pitches).

The Classical period was a time of great experimentation for wind instrument makers. Extra keys were added to the instruments and bore tapers were modified. This process was very much by trial and error.

FOCUS ON...

a flute by Richard Potter

This is an early transverse flute by the London maker, Richard Potter, dated about 1782. It is made in 4 sections of boxwood with ivory mounts. It has three interchangeable body sections, known as "corps-de-rechange" so that the musician can play in a variety of common pitches. Potter was born in Mitcham, Surrey in 1726. In 1745 he set up shop in Green Dragon Court, Cheapside, where he specialized in flute making. He was an innovative craftsman with many new inventions and patents related to the refinement of the design of instruments. His skill and craftsmanship were held in such high esteem that an industry evolved faking bogus copies of his instruments. These came to be known as "Bastard Potters" and can be identified by mis-spelling of his name on the makers mark.

18th century one-keyed flute
This style was common through from 1700 until about 1820 and is known as a Baroque flute.

Keys were developed to cover the tone holes in place of the fingers; they were useful because they could be left to close the tone hole even when the player's fingers were not covering them.

The 19th century was a time of great regional diversity in flute making across Europe and North America. The typically German 8 key flute is particularly visually distinctive with its ivory head, blackwood body and matching piccolo-sized instrument. This type of instrument was known as a 'reform flute' and often had more than eight keys. From the mid-19th century a variety of different system flutes were being produced in different geographical areas and by different makers: for example, in America as well as Central and Eastern Europe the 'Meyer' model was particularly popular. There are many examples of extended flutes that fall into this category.

The term 'System flutes' refer to those where an effort has been made to rationalize the keywork. They can be divided into two categories: those with a cylindrical shaped bore and those with a conical bore. Until the invention and adoption of the cylindrical Boehm system in 1847, flutes of the 18th and 19th centuries generally had conical bores.

OTHER FLUTES

In addition to the more familiar types of flute, the Collection also holds a number of interesting variants on the theme. These include the oddly-jointed Burghley flutes. It is thought that these instruments were devised and made by Burghley, Camden Town in London in the late 19th century. They never enjoyed the kind of broad popularity that would ensure any contemporary interest. Even stranger are the Giorgi Flutes. This is a slightly more popular family of instruments that were patented in 1897.

FOCUS ON...

the Boehm system flute

The new Boehm system flute was developed in a number of stages. Theobald Boehm of Munich began by using open standing keys (keys which remained open when the player's fingers were not holding them closed) in place of the earlier closed standing keys. He also increased the size of the tone holes and placed them differently in accordance with the instrument's acoustics; improving both the tonality and volume of the instrument. The conical flute by Boehm dated c.1840 is an example of some of these earlier modifications and experiments in Munich.

Boehm re-designed his flute in 1847 and this basic design, with a few modifications, is used all over the world today. Boehm still wanted to increase the volume of the low notes and was concerned about the instrument's intonation in the third octave. His original inspiration for this may have been the pioneering work of the English maker Nicholson, who enlarged the embouchure and tone holes of the instruments to increase the volume. Boehm changed the shape of the bore to cylindrical, which allowed him to increase the size of the tone holes further. As fingers would struggle to cover the enlarged holes, solid key cups and pads were adopted shortly after this. The head joint of Boehm's flute was tapered at this stage, to counteract the effect of changing the shape of the bore, which resulted in the octaves not being perfectly in tune. French and English makers were quick to adopt the new system: in London, Rudall and Rose were among the first and there are examples by them in the Collection.

Boehm-system flute dated 1850
This demonstrates the rationalised design and incorporated a G# key.

detail
of keys

Very simple in design, they had little keywork but were designed so that they could play in any key. Commonly, they were made of an early plastic called "ebonite". This would be their downfall as it is an unstable form of vulcanized rubber that deteriorates with the introduction of warm, moist air.

CLARINETS

Around 1700, the German maker Johann Christoph Denner developed the clarinet by converting one of the chalumeau's keys into a register key, allowing the instrument to be played in the upper register. Denner's clarinet had a total of two keys. For a while, the chalumeau continued to be used to play pieces in the lower register alongside the clarinet as early clarinets did not play so well in the lower register.

Clarinets constitute a family of musical instruments with single reeds. By far the most common is the Bb soprano clarinet, but there are instruments from many of the different members of the family on display in the Collection, including smaller 'piccolo' clarinets, alto clarinets and basset horns. The example by Willems is a 2 key clarinet in F; it may be one of the earliest clarinets in the Collection. In addition there are clarinets in C and Bb, most of which were made in England and France. The clarinet was gradually improved by the addition of further keys, which increased its range and allowed for easier fingerings.

Also in the Collection is a clarinet dated c1800 by Heinrich Grenser, who invented an early form of the bass clarinet known as the Basset Horn. By the classical period the clarinet had eight tone holes and five keys. This became the standard design for most of the early instruments' use, during the period 1760 – 1820. Mozart was

SINGLE REED

The clarinet was developed from the chalumeau, an early instrument with a single reed and with similarities to the recorder and the clarinet. The chalumeau could only be played in the lower register.

Grenser

"..MUST WE FIND TRUE PERFECTION OF THIS BEAUTIFUL INSTRUMENT."

Heinrich Grenser was born in Lipprechtsroda, Germany, in March 1764. He was a member of a noted and respected family of musical instrument makers and was apprenticed to his uncle in 1779. He took over the workshop in 1796. He was an inventor and intelligent designer and spent some time in the development of bass-clarinets. He was also a correspondent and commentator on instrument design. In 1800 he wrote, "Not in the number of keys, no, but in the greater simplicity of the flute, without sacrificing its elegance, must we find true perfection of this beautiful instrument". Several hundred of his instruments survive in public and private collections.

particularly fond of the instrument and wrote several pieces for it.

A major innovation was brought about by Iwan Müller, who in 1812 invented a new type of pad cover for the clarinet's tone holes. The new pads were completely airtight, allowing the number of keys on the instrument to be increased significantly. The clarinet could now play in any key, and the instrument began to be made with thirteen keys and seven finger holes. Eugene Albert and Carl Baermann developed their own fingering and key systems for the clarinet based on Müller's work, though they mostly fell out of use by the early 20th century. A late 19th century clarinet by Eugene Albert is on display.

CLARINET KEYWORK

Boehm's system developed for flutes (discussed above) also impacted on clarinet design of the 19th century.

Hyacinthe Klosé and Buffet adapted Boehm's keying system to suit the clarinet, allowing for simpler fingering, between 1839 and 1843. The system did not catch on immediately as players had to relearn the instruments. Clarinettists of Germany and Austria continue to use clarinets such as those designed by Müller, called the Oehler system. Examples of these instruments can be found on display in the Collection. Elsewhere, the Boehm system as adapted by Klosé and Buffet, is almost universal and only a few modifications have been made to it since the mid 19th century. Early simple system clarinets by Louis-Auguste Buffet and Buffet Crampon are on display along with those by Eugene Albert, Boosey & Co and a pair of clarinets dated to c1900 by Rudall Carte. More modern systems are also represented including the plastic Lyons instrument of the 1990s.

Saint Cecilia, the patron saint of music

This image is based on the painting by the Rennaissnce artist Raphael. It demostrates, through the broken instruments, the disunity of all things.

the Contrabass Clarinet

Amongst some of the more iconic clarinets in the collection we have the "contrabass" pedal clarinet by Besson of London. The contrabass clarinet is the largest member of the clarinet family in common use. This instrument is made of maple with white bronze crook and nickel keywork. It is described as being a "simple" system, with a covered action that only goes down as far a low E. It was formerly in the Adam Carse collection, the bulk of which is now held by the Horniman Museum. According to records, it was originally owned by the Royal Military School of Music at Kneller Hall.

Besson was originally a firm of French brass instrument makers that was founded in Paris by Gustave Auguste Besson in 1837 or 1838, when he was 17-18 years old. The London branch of the firm was opened in 1851 to coincide with the Great Exhibition at South Kensington. The different branches of the firm broke away in the 1890's. The British branch was taken over by Boosey & Hawkes in 1948 while the French branch ceased business in 1994.

The keywork is an example of ergonomic instrument design with the intention of improving the facility of the instrument for musicians.

Unlike most clarinets this instrument has an expanding bore profile which has a profound effect on the tonal qualities.

Contrabass clarinet
These instruments are generally uncommon and not very often seen outside large orchestras.

the Ivory Clarinet in C

The ivory clarinet was part of the original Philip Bate gift, donated to the Collection in 1970. There is no maker's mark but it is thought to date from the first quarter of the 19th century. This is based on a number of stylistic elements including the shape of the keywork and the overall profile. Nowadays the trade in ivory is subject to control as part of the Convention on International Trade in Endangered Species of Wild Fauna and Flora (CITES Treaty). So it would no longer be possible or defensible to make instruments out of this material.

There has been a lot of debate regarding the importance of the use of particular materials in wind instrument construction. Some musicians and reporters are adamant that material characterization has a central and crucial role in the unique tonal and playing qualities of instruments. Others maintain that this is not the case and cannot be claimed categorically as there are too many variables to be able to test the acoustical model. The closest researchers have been to answering this question has been a series of "blind-testing" experiments in which musicians have been challenged to express an opinion on materials whilst not being able to see the instrument being played.

Seven-keyed clarinet in C
The profile is typical of late 18th-early 19th century instruments with the addition of extra keys.

SAXOPHONES

The saxophone is a relatively modern development and was invented in 1846 by the famous Belgian instrument maker Adolphe Sax. His understanding of clarinets and interest in the ophicleide (Greek for "Keyed-Serpent") led to the creation of the saxophone, which uses a single-reed mouthpiece like that of the clarinet. Sax modelled the keywork on the systems devised for clarinets and oboes. By the early 1840s Sax had made saxophones of various different sizes. It was originally designed to be used in military bands and gained huge popularity in this field. However, its possibilities in other musical genres soon became evident and now it can be found across the whole musical spectrum. Today the most popular ones are those pitched at Bb and Eb. On display is an Eb instrument made by Adolphe Sax himself in Paris, c.1859. Also in the Collection is a later instrument made in 1907 by Sax's son; Adolphe Edouard.

FOCUS ON...

the Grafton Saxophone

The Grafton saxophone was a plastic alto saxophone that was invented by Hector Sommaruga, an Italian living in London. It was injection moulded, which meant that only alto's were made. The technology proved too difficult for larger instruments. The name of the instrument came from Sommaruga's address; "Grafton Way", where he worked in the late 1940's. At £55 the retail cost of the instrument was less than half that of a conventional brass instrument. It came to be very popular at the time and was famously played by such saxophone virtuosi as Charlie Parker, John Dankworth and Ornette Coleman. The instrument has a number of fundamental problems relating to the brittle nature of the plastic material. However, it has never been criticized on account of its tonal or playing qualities.

An early plastic design
Modern materials have enabled many other instruments to be made of plactic including trumpets and trombones.

OBOES AND SHAWMS

The oboe is a double-reed instrument. It has a narrow conical bore and was developed from the shawm family of instruments. The oboe was made in three pieces from the Baroque period onwards. Like the clarinet and the recorder, the oboe is part of a family of instruments, which includes the cor anglais and the oboe d'amore, among others. Before 1770, the instrument was called the hautbois (French for 'high wood'). The oboe's ancestor is the shawm, which was first made in Europe in the 12th century. Examples of the shawm family of instruments can be seen in the collection. The shawm is usually made all in one piece and has a wide conical bore.

FOCUS ON...

the Richters Oboe

Hendrik Richters was from a family of oboe-makers. He was born in Amsterdam in about 1683, the son of Frederick Richters from Munster in Germany. Hendrik became known for making some of the most skillfully elegant instruments of the period. He specialized exclusively in highly decorated oboes. The Richters oboe on display is made of ebony, ivory and silver and is very highly decorated. These high-status materials indicate that this instrument was intended for a wealthy client and perhaps, not a professional musician. When it is compared with an oboe of the same period by Stanesby Junior we see two polar opposites of the 18th century design aesthetic. The Richters is highly decorated compared to which the Stanesby Junior demonstates a profound restraint.

The body is made of turned ebony.

Baroque oboe
In the highly decorative Rococo style with knurled ivory ferrules and engraved silver key work.

The Collection contains what is thought to be the oldest oboe in Britain; it is c1690 and is widely known as the 'Galpin Oboe'. The maker is unknown, but it seems it is either French or English in origin. The Bate also holds the Hendrik Richters oboe dated c1700, which is also of exceptionally fine craftsmanship. Most oboes of the Baroque period were made of boxwood and had 2 keys. Also on display is the much simpler in style two-key English oboe by Stanesby Jr. dated to 1750. Stanesby was one of the leading woodwind instrument makers in Europe during his lifetime and his work was much sought after. (see Focus on Thomas Stanesby Junior)

COR ANGLAIS

The cor anglais is pitched in F and is essentially the oboe's big brother. The fingering and playing technique for the cor anglais is very similar to that of the oboe and in consequence most oboists do not find it difficult to play the larger instrument. Early versions were curved or angled in shape to allow the player's fingers to reach the tone holes. Modern keying systems have made this curve unnecessary. It is thought that this may be one of the origins of the name of the instruments, ie: "Angled Horn" (rather than "English Horn").

OTHER LARGE OBOES

There are also other members of the oboe family in the Collection, such as the hautbois baryton and the oboe d'amore. There is also an early tenor oboe made by the much-emulated Belgian woodwind instrument maker Jean-Hyacinthe Joseph Rottenburgh.

A broken consort
Rennaisance wind
instrumentalists play
a flute, a cornet and a
rauschpfeife

the Cor Anglais by Fornari

This instrument was made by Andrea Fornari of Venice in the late 18th or early 19th century. The instrument has been made in sections consisting of two carved halves that have been glued together and then covered in leather. The leather has been decorated and the key-work has been made of ivory. This is plainly a high-status instrument and conforms very well to the design of the period. 27 examples by this maker survive in public collections dating from between 1792 and 1825.

Curved body
This design allows the musician to reach the tone holes and was common before the development of system keywork.

BASSOONS

The bassoon was developed during the baroque period. Its predecessor is generally considered to be the curtal, which was a double reed instrument with its reed attached to a metal crook. Like the bassoon, the curtal had a conical bore, which doubled back on itself. Around 1650, bassoons began to be made in several sections, allowing for greater accuracy in the circumference of the internal bore profile, this being crucial to the fundamental acoustics of the instrument. At around this time extra keys were added to the instrument, extending its range down to Bb. Pioneering instrument maker Martin Hotteterre, along with other French makers of the period, is usually credited with this evolution. In the early 18th century, a fourth key was added. The earliest bassoon in the Collection dates to c.1720; it has

FOCUS ON...

the Sharp Family by Zoffany

The Bate Collection houses all of the surviving instruments shown in Zoffany's portrait of the Sharp family. These include: two Bb clarinets made by George Miller c.1770; two boxwood flageolets by John Mason dating to 1750; and a pair of 18th century horns by Hofmaster, an instrument maker based in London. A copy of the portrait is displayed on the wall of the corridor which houses the majority of the collection's woodwind instruments.

four keys and was made by Dondeine, probably a French manufacturer. There are also many examples of English bassoons by Thomas Cahusac senior, Milhouse, Miller, Gerock and Kusder.

The Collection includes a systematic selection of 19th and 20th century instruments, these include smaller tenoroon instruments and a variety of larger contrabassoons from French and German workshops and factories. There are several fine Parisian examples by Jean-Nicolas Savary, Besson and Mahillon here from the early 19th century. Around the middle of the 19th century bassoon manufacture was increasingly divided into two schools, developing independently. In Germany, the Heckel system began to be developed by Almenräder, Weber and Heckel, who aimed to improve intonation and re-arrange the keywork. For two generations, Heckel's descendants continued to refine the bassoon, gaining in popularity by the 20th century, despite other Boehm-style systems. In France, however, the bassoon was developed more gradually. This style of bassoon is called the Buffet system and was still used in this country, along with the more popular Heckel system, until the 1980s.

CRUMHORNS

Crumhorns are double reed woodwind instruments that were particularly popular in the Renaissance period. Their distinctive name comes from the German for 'bent horn', the relevance of which is immediately apparent given the instrument's J shape. They are capped reed instruments, requiring the player to blow into a wind cap on which the double reed is mounted in order to produce a note. The instrument has a relatively limited range, so was often played in a group with instruments of differing sizes. The Collection holds an example, which is generally regarded as being the oldest in Britain and is thought to date from about 1600. It was constructed in two longitudinal halves, rather similar to the early cor anglais construction style, and is covered in leather. The Collection includes many other modern-copy instruments mostly made in the 1970s.

BAGPIPES

There have been tantilisingly obscure mentions of bagpipe-like instruments dating back to antiquity, as reported by Aristophanes in 4,000 BCE. In the 14th century bagpipes were used in courtly music in England, though this gradually died out and they moved northwards and westwards. Despite the prevalence of the modern Scottish Great Highland Bagpipe, bagpipes are popular across a large part of Europe and North Africa and are used particularly in the production of folk music. Bagpipes usually have a chanter and one or more drones which are supplied with air from a bag, which is placed under the player's arm and compressed. More refined versions are bellow-blown.

14th century bagpiper
This is a mouthpipe-blown instrument.

brass

instruments

INTRODUCTION TO BRASS MUSICAL INSTRUMENTS

Brass musical instruments are a form of wind instrument that produce sound by a sympathetic vibration of air in a tube according to the vibration of the player's lips. Technically, they are all termed "Labrosones" (or lip-reed instruments) and share a number of acoustical features with reed instruments. Despite the commonly-used name (Brass instruments) they don't actually need to be made of brass and instruments of this type have been know to be made in a variety of metals, wood, bone, horn and ivory, glass and ceramics. More recent developments have seen instruments made of plastics. There are several strands of brass instrument type. Perhaps the more familiar ones would include horns, trumpets, trombones, cornets and tubas. The Bate Collection also includes a broad range of other types including cornetti, serpents, ophicleides, saxhorns and others. They come in a range of sizes, materials, shapes and styles but all share a similar acoustical model characterized by the mouthpiece.

A waites band
Including fanfare
trumpets and sackbuts.

HORNS

The Bate Collection has a particularly fine collection
of historical horns. These had been amassed, over
the years by the eminent collector and horn expert

FOCUS ON...

the Raoux Cor Solo

This instrument is from the Paris
workshop of the famous Raoux family
of brass instrument makers. They were
especially noted for their hand-horns,
which they raised to the highest standard
of design and workmanship. The horn is
an improved version of a previous design
known as Hampl-Werner Inventionshorn.
In this, the instrument has a fixed
mouthpipe with centrally inserted crooks
as opposed to other designs with interchangeable mouth-crooks. The crooks
were made so the instrument could be
played in the keys of D, Eb, E, F and G, the
most usual keys for solo playing, and was
therefore known as the Cor Solo. It was

an immensely successful design and was
adopted by many leading virtuosi including
Thurrschmidt, LeBrun, Palsa, Punto and
Puzzi. This instrument and crooks were
made in 1823. It was donated to the Bate
Collection in 1972 by William Morley-
Pegge as a memorial to his late father,
the noted horn player and organologist
Reginald Morley-Pegge.

The cor solo
A highly-refined design of a classical natural
hand-horn.

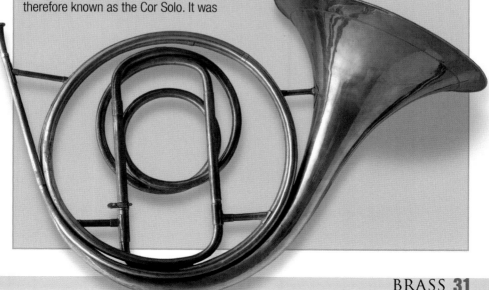

FOCUS ON...

the Omnitonic Horn

This instrument was patented by John Callcott in 1851 and probably made by Thomas Key, London, at that date. This was one of the continuing efforts to improve the intonation of the instrument and to achieve perfect chromaticism. Any pitch can be selected by plugging the central radial pipe into the appropriate socket, from Bb basso in the centre to Bb alto nearest the tuning slide. The virtue of the omnitonic horn was that it remained a hand horn and yet had all possible crooks built into the instrument. However, the process of uncoupling the radial pipe, selecting a new socket and then re-coupling it is so cumbersome that it was not terribly successful as an orchestral instrument.

Callcott's Radius French Horn
One of many designs to resolve the crisis of chromaticism in natural brass instruments.

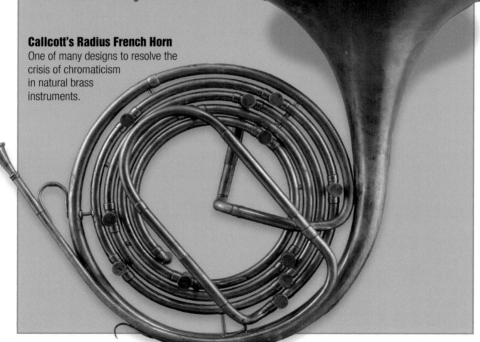

Reginald Morley-Pegge. Many of them feature in his seminal work: *"The French Horn: Some notes on the evolution of the instrument and of its technique."*. As such, the collection has become a primary resource for

French Horn scholars and they are able to refer to the original instruments, which have been retained in the condition that they were in when the book was authored in 1960.

Traditionally the horn was associated with hunting, often used to call hounds to the hunt. It was not until the 19th century that the horn was equipped with valves. Before this, the note was determined by the player's varying lip pressure and only those within the harmonic series could be played. Horns without valves are generally known as natural horns. There are a number of examples in the Collection dating from the mid-18th century onwards. A French concert horn by Lucien-Joseph Raoux is also displayed, along with its full set of crooks, interchangeable sections of tubing of different lengths, which could be used to allow the horn to play in different keys.

From about 1815 onwards, horns began to be made with valves, which not only avoided the necessity of changing crooks midway through a performance, but also made the horn fully chromatic. 19th century examples of valved horns can be seen on display by Austrian, German and English makers. Most of these valved horns use rotary valves, which were first developed in the early 19th century. Particularly interesting is John Callcott's omnitonic horn of 1851 which has all of the crooks built into the instrument.

TRUMPETS

The trumpet is regarded as being one of the most ancient of instruments and examples were found when the tomb of the Pharoah Tutankhamun was uncovered by Howard Carter in 1922. These instruments certainly are over 3,500 years old. In

FOCUS ON...

the Simon Beale Trumpet, 1667

This instrument was made in 1666 by trumpeter Simon Beale. During the civil war and the Protectorate Beale was state trumpeter to Oliver Cromwell. Following the restoration of the monarchy he was appointed as state trumpeter to Charles II. This instrument shows design features that suggest that Beale had done some collaborative work with Charles' other main trumpeter, William Bull, who had accompanied the king during his exile in Europe and had picked up many continental fashions. In later life it became the "luck" of Woodenham Hall. During the late 19th and early 20th century it was used by the butler to summon the household and guests to dinner. In its current form the instrument has been soldered together so that the joints cannot be removed. Analysis of the metal has shown that the bell is probably not original, although use of the profile in copies has shown that it works very well indeed. The mouthpiece is very large (almost the size of a trombone mouthpiece) and is also soldered to the mouthpipe. X-Ray analysis has shown that it has no back-bore, which means that modern players have great difficulty with intonation.

Early Baroque casting based on continental European designs.

A natural trumpet
This design is very successful and still in use today as a fanfare trumpet by the Household Cavalry

the Medieval period trumpets were mostly used for signalling and military purposes and were therefore very important to the army. At this time trumpet-playing was a closely guarded art and instruction occurred in selective guilds. It was a high-status activity and closely related to kingship and royalty. Writing in *Il Principe* in 1513, Niccolò Machiavelli advised that *"The New Prince would authorize the use of the trumpet for the use of chevaliers"* as opposed to the common public.

PLAYING TECHNIQUE

Embouchure (lip tension) is used to alter the note of a brass instrument. Later valves and slides could be used to change the pitch by redirecting the air-flow through a different length of tubing.

Like horns, early trumpets were without valves and so were only able to play notes within the harmonic series. In the Baroque period the trumpet gained repute as a virtuoso instrument with the upper register being developed by trumpeters such as Cesare Bendinelli. The French composer Jean Baptiste Lully (1632 – 1687) wrote extensively for trumpets, raising the instrument to full orchestral use. By the beginning of the 18th century trumpets regularly appeared in popular musical performances. In 1717 Georg Frederic Handel famously featured them in the first performance of the Water Music. By the 1760s the instrument was well established as a part of the wind-harmony music being developed by Mozart and Haydn. In modern times the trumpet covers all musical genres and has many exponents in Jazz and popular music.

The trompette demilune is a type of trumpet designed by Dubois & Cie. It is deliberately curved to allow for hand stopping, a technique used by players to reduce the pitch of a note by a semitone, allowing

the Cornet Simple or Circular Trumpet by Jahn of Paris

This is a natural trumpet by D Jahn of Paris, dated about 1820. In appearance, it resembles the construction of the later natural horns. There has been some debate amongst experts as to whether this instrument is a trumpet or a cornet. It is a circular model, with a single round loop. The highly decorated interior of the bell has been painted with gold floral design on red. It is accompanied by a selection of crooks, which are all conical. It is here that the mystery lies. The body of the instrument and the mouthpiece are very trumpet-like, while the crooks and the bell-flare more closely resemble a cornet construction. In addition to the unique design, there is some evidence of hand-stopping technique. It comes in a box with a set of crooks (like an orchestral hand-horn of the period).

An unfamiliar trumpet design
This enables musicians to handstop in the bell of the instrument to achieve semi-tones.

for notes outside the instrument's harmonic series. Another design innovation features on 18th and 19th century slide trumpets, which allow a further series of options for extra notes. By the 19th century, trumpets began to be made with valves, which increased the number of possible notes. There are several 19th century instruments by Charles Mahillon, which use Périnet valves, a type of piston valve invented in

1838 by François Périnet. Some of the instruments also use rotary valves, a feature that has become a popular choice for German musicians. There is also a reproduction of a key trumpet on display, which uses a system of keys to redirect the air-flow, as opposed to valves. These trumpets were relatively common before the invention of valve trumpets.

TROMBONES

The name trombone is of Italian origin and simply means "Large Trumpet". The trombone is probably the least changed of all the brass instruments with modern versions bearing a resemblance to their historical counterpart. During early music periods it was referred to in English as the sackbut. The origins of this name are vague but are thought to come from the French sacqueboute, meaning "to pull and to push". A set of three German trombones, dating to 1814, are on display and are known as the "Waterloo Sackbuts". They are of particular interest to makers as they have not been finely finished and the marks of manufacture can be plainly seen. Included on display is an ornately decorated tenor trombone from the second half of the 19th century. Its maker, Joseph Higham of Manchester, made many instruments for military bands. The Collection includes a selection of valve trombones, which were popular during the 19th century. One of their main uses was for mounted musicians in cavalry bands. They were designed in a variety of forms, each addressing issues of comfort, relative playability when sitting on a jogging horse or other ergonomic matters. However, modern mounted bands have mostly reverted to using slide trombones.

FOCUS ON...

Joseph Higham

Joseph Higham was born in Manchester in 1818. In 1842 he established his instrument-making business at 127 Strangeways. He was the first maker to give instruments as prizes at contests, and in 1860 founded the band of the 1st Manchester Volunteer Battalion. He was an innovative inventor and always sought to improve on the design of valves and slides to enhance the tonal qualities of the instruments he made. Perhaps his most eccentric contribution was the patented "Highamphone" which was a combination of euphonium and valve trombone. Higham instruments had a distinctive sound that was closely associated with the Brass Band movement. Because of this, many Higham instruments are still in use today.

The Higham factory
This method of instrument making was still in use in England until the 21st century.

CORNETS

Cornets originated in France in about 1820, when the instrument was developed from the coiled post horn. Unlike the trumpet, the cornet has a mostly conical bore, which gives it quite a different tone to that of a trumpet. The earliest cornet on display dates to 1830 and was made by Marcel August Raoux. It has two piston valves and a G crook. A cornet dating back to 1845 by George MacFarlane demonstrates his clapper key, which improved trills and was patented in the same year. Cornopean was the early name for a cornet, many of which used the Stözel valve system.

One of the most popular cornets in the collection is the Echo Cornet by Brown & Sons of London, dated about 1895. It has a fourth valve that diverts the playing length of the instrument to an integrated "mute bell". This feature could provide the effect of the instrument playing near and far and was used in comic opera and other light entertainment pieces.

BUGLES

Bugles are mostly known today as a form of signalling or band instrument used in the military of various countries around the world. In the Middle Ages an old French word 'buglaret' was derived from the Latin for bullock. In English the word meant 'wild ox'. From this the bugle can be seen to be derived from the use of animal horns. It is one of the least complex brass instruments. Like the natural trumpet, the bugle has a limited range of notes, known as the harmonic series; traditionally it has had no valves, unlike other modern brass instruments. This is beginning to change with the development of more sophisticated bugle-bands in the United States, which incorporate instruments with full valve systems. This enduring programme began in the mid-19th century when some makers experimented with using them on the bugle. These became popular with the Italian Bersaglieri regiments and are still in use with them.

The modern bugle in copper or brass is in extensive use by the armed forces and civilian youth bands. The instrument design comes from about 1800 and was developed from the German hunting horn, which was in use in North America. It has now been adopted across the globe.

The Bate also has a fine collection of early 19th century keyed bugles. This design was intended to extend the musical range. These instruments continued to be made well into the middle of the century and were used along with valve instruments. There was a stage in the history and development of the brass band tradition when competitions were held to explore the virtuoso possibilities of both types of instrument.

FOCUS ON...

the Shaw Bugle

Displayed in the Bate are a number of bugles made by European makers from Italy, Sweden and France. The Collection includes an early bugle by the family of London makers William Shaw and Sons. The instrument on display is pitched in C, although it does have a Bb crook. This bugle is one of the oldest in the collection and dates to the early 19th century when the familiar coiled bugle design became popular. Prior to this period the bugle design was based on that of the German hunting horn. The instrument differs from its modern counterpart in that the overall conical profile of the bore progression is much more pronounced. Tonally, this means that the lower frequencies of the harmonic series have a higher amplitude giving the instrument a more horn-like tone. Images of instruments like this can be found in contemporary illustrations from the beginning of the 19th century as it gained use as a military signalling instrument.

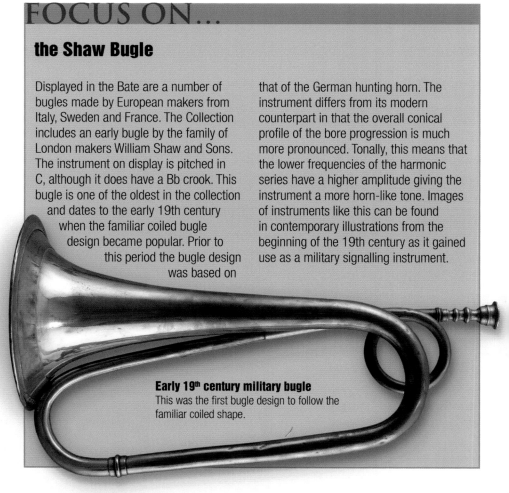

Early 19th century military bugle
This was the first bugle design to follow the familiar coiled shape.

FOCUS ON...

the Halari Keyed Bugle

The French firm of Halari (founded in 1768) were makers and inventors of brass instruments. They particularly focused on the development of orchestral horns but by the beginning of the 19th century were exploring other instrumental forms. In 1821 they patented the Clavitube, a seven-keyed brass bugle. This is an example of that type of instrument. These instruments were common in most military bands of the period and very soon came to be used in orchestras and other ensembles.

Side hole brass
These instruments were a transitional design between natural brass and more advanced valve technology.

SAXHORNS

The saxhorns were patented by Adolphe Sax in 1845, leading to various disputes and lawsuits by other musical instrument makers who claimed to have invented the instrument. Saxhorns form a family of seven instruments and, like saxophones, they are pitched in Bb and Eb. The saxhorns were originally developed for use by the army and have come to revolutionise the modern military band. The term 'saxhorn' has now become applied so loosely as to have no significance and refers to a broad variety of instruments. Several saxhorns made by Adolphe Sax in the mid-19th century are held in the Collection, including one designed to be used by cavalry.

FOCUS ON...

the Key Serpent

One of the more noted instruments in the Collection is a military serpent. This instrument was made by the wind instrument maker Thomas Key in 1813. Key was most famous for making brass instruments such as bugles and valve horns but his portfolio included other instruments such as flutes, bass horns and military serpents. In 1809 he was listed as musical instrument maker "to their Royal Highnesses the Prince of Wales, Dukes of York, Kent, Cumberland and Cambridge."

This serpent is fairly typical of an English-style military serpent. It is of sectioned wooden construction in the classic "S" bend arrangement with all parts stapled together and then bound in linen and painted with black pitch. There are six open tone holes and seven brass keys mounted on saddles. The brass crook fits into a brass socket ferrule which bears the engraving: "KEY / 20 CHARING CROSS / LONDON ; LGL5 from 1813". The bends are supported by brass struts and the bell is angled forwards at about 40 degrees. It is complete with an ivory mouthpiece and is in playable condition.

What is particularly interesting about this instrument is that the brass bell mount also bears an engraving: "RICHARD BENTINCK / -DRUMMER- / 23RD REGIMENT OF FOOT / - R•W•F - / WELLINGTON - WATERLOO / JUNE 18TH 1815". That is an exciting piece of evidence and would tend to give us a fairly unshakeable provenance of the instrument from the time it was made. Recently Richard Bentinck's memoirs have been published in which he mentions using the instrument in the Waterloo campaign.

SERPENTS

The serpent is regarded as both a successful instrument and also a failure, according to the tastes of the composers and listening audience. Famously, Handel hated the istrument and refused to score for it. The serpent has its origins in France at the end of 16th century, when it was used to strengthen church choirs. Its inventor is said to be Edmé Guillaume who developed it from the cornett. The body of the instrument flows in an elegant, sinuous curving plane and is a most striking design. It differs significantly

Miltary serpent
by Thomas Key. This instrument is
still in playing condition and has
recently been used in the BBC
Promenade Concerts, at the Albert
Hall.

from the design of its ancestor instrument, the
cornett, in size, scope and bore taper, all of which
contribute to its fringe popularity. There has been a
rise in popularity of the instrument in recent years
with many recordings, compositions and concerts.
The Collection includes examples of the keyless,
church serpent and the keyed military serpent.

The Collection also includes a mid-19th century serpent which was taken apart by Philip Bate, who had originally intended to restore the instrument. Instead, he decided to display it as evidence of the serpent's construction in England at this time. Sections would be made of wood and the whole body of the instrument was then covered in canvas and painted with pitch to seal any leaks.

Other instruments in the early bass brass family include Serpent Forveilles, bass-horns and the very rare 'Royal Patent Hibernicon' that was designed to be played in the upper register. This is one of only two instruments that were ever made of this type. The location of the other is unknown.

FOCUS ON...

the Turton Ophicleide

The ophicleide is a technical development from the serpent in order to improve the tonal quality and intonation. The name is a Greek construction meaning "Keyed-Serpent". The keys were the crucial improvement on the design and allowed the player much greater accuracy in chromaticism. Turton made this instrument in Dublin, Ireland, in 1829. It is based on a design by Halary of Paris and has 11 flat cup keys. The ophicleide continued to be featured as an instrument in orchestral works long after it had been superceded by valved tubas. Hector Louis Berlioz scored for it in the Symphonie Fantastique and it continued to be used in Brazilian Choro bands well into the 20th century.

Keyed serpent
This design was the inspriation for the development of the saxophone. Adolphe Sax experimented with clarinet mouthpieces and came up with an almost perfect acoustical model.

TUBAS

The tuba is the deepest of the modern, valved brass instruments. It was invented by Prussian makers Wilhelm Friedrich Wieprecht and Johann Gottfried Moritz in 1835 and was inspired by and drew on the features of the serpent and the saxhorn. Originally the tuba was primarily a military instrument and was particularly popular in marching bands before 1900. Nowadays it is used across a wide variety of musical genres, including the large romantic orchestras. It gained a certain amount of fame as a solo instrument when it featured in the Gerard Hoffnung concert series during the 1950s and early 1960s.

The pitch and the style of the tuba varies a lot depending on the country of origin. The mid-19th century tuba by Johann Heinrich Zetsche, Hanover is pitched in F as is typical for German tubas. There are also two bass tubas by the London makers: one by Boosey and one by Hawkes. They are pitched in F and BBb respectively.

THE TUBA FAMILY

Tuba is sometimes used to describe a number of different brass instruments including the sousaphone and the helicon. The Bate has examples of many of these.

The helicon emerged in Austria around 1849 and there are two displayed in the Collection, one of which is perhaps French and the other, American. When in playing position, the helicon was placed over the head, with the tubing under the player's right arm, essentially circling the player. They were originally designed for use in cavalry bands and spread to wider use until it was discovered that they caused breathing difficulties for the musicians. This was also the design which inspired American bandmaster John Philip Sousa in the invention of the eponymous sousaphone, much in use by bands internationally.

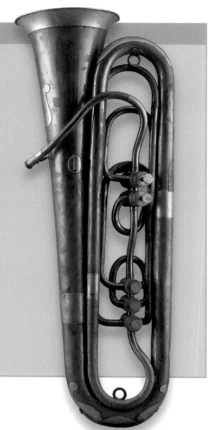

FOCUS ON...

the F Bass Tuba by Zetche

This instrument was made in the mid 19th century by Johann Heinriche Zetche of Hanover. It is in high-pitch 'F' and has 5 Berlin-type valves. This design was originally developed by Stötzel in 1827 and then further improved by the Berlin band leader Weiprecht in 1828. According to the inscription on the bell of the instrument it was used by the Hanoverian Guards Regiment. This places the instrument prior to the Austro-Prussian war of 1866 following which the Kingdom of Hanover was absorbed into the Prussian state.

A highly ornate design
This early bass brass instrument features an uncommon number of valves and a variety of decorative cartouches.

CORNETTS

Like crumhorns and recorders, cornetts also have their origins in the Medieval period, though they were particularly popular between 1550-1700. The cornett is the ancestor of most modern brass instruments and particularly the trumpet, although medieval cornetts were frequently made from leather covered wood. In England, cornetts only began to be used more frequently during the early 17th century and two instruments on display in the Collection date to this period. One is a treble cornett and the other a smaller cornettino and both are slightly curved. There are also reproductions of the straight mute cornett (particularly popular in Venice) and the

more serpentine tenor cornett, which was pitched
a fifth lower than the treble. The cornett is said to
be a particularly difficult instrument to play for the
modern musician as the small wind-style mouthpiece
requires a specialist embouchure.

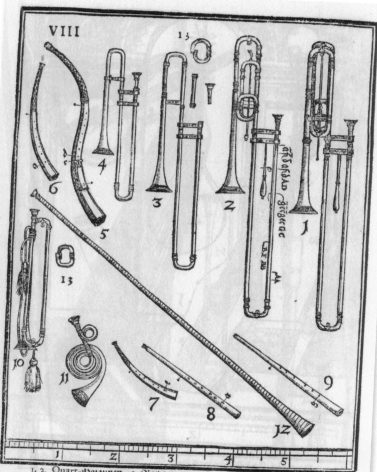

1. 2. Quart-Poſaunen. 3. Rechte gemeine Poſaun. 4. Alt-Poſaun. 5. Corno/
Groß Tenor-Cornet. 6. Recht ChorZinck. 7. Klein DiſcantZinck / ſo ein Quint höher.
8. GeraderZinck mit ein Mundſtück. 9. StillZinck. 10. Trommet. 11. Jäger Trommet.
12. Hölgern Trommet. 13. Krumbbügel auff ein gantz Thon.

Praetorious syntagma
This woodcut from 1619 features trumpets, horns, sackbutts and cornetts.

INTRODUCTION TO STRING INSTRUMENTS

The Bate has a variety of string instruments representative of all the main strands of European art and folk music. These can be divided between plucked instruments and bowed instruments. The plucked instruments include lutes, mandolins and guitars. The bowed instruments include the violin family and also the viola da gamba family.

Many of the plucked string instruments on display can be traced back to the lute. This type of instrument originated from the Arabic oud (meaning 'wood'), which was introduced to Europe via the Moors in the Medieval period. The English guitar on display is typical of the late 18th century, by which time the lute had fallen out of popularity. The guitar was cheaper to make and easier to play than the lute, and so appealed to far more people.

The Collection also houses a highly decorated guitar. It is probably French and dates to the early-19th century. It is an example of the Spanish guitar type, from which our modern guitar is ultimately derived.

Early 17th century lutenist
The lute was derived from the Arabic oud and achieved wide popularity as a solo courtly instrument.

CONSORTS OF BOWED STRINGS

The violin and viol families were created during the renaissance. These instruments were played together in groups and were known as consorts.

16th century woodcut
This print portrays a variety of contemporary bowed and plucked instruments.

The bowed string instruments can be divided between the instruments of the violin family, which include violins, violas and cellos and other types of bowed string instruments such as viols. The violin design we are aware of today is derived from the types of instruments being made in the Cremonese workshops of the great Italian makers. The instruments in the Bate Collection have been 'set-up' to reflect the style of instrument being used during the 18th century and can be used to form a baroque string quartet. Among the instruments is a violin that has been crafted from the material remains of an earlier viola-d'amore. The body shape differed considerably from the 'classic' style. The violin by Robert Thompson has a later carved capital thought to represent Georgiana Cavendish, Duchess of Devonshire.

The earliest evidence for bowed string instruments in Europe is the lira of the 9th century Byzantine Empire. During the 11th and 12th centuries the lira, along with the Islamic rebab, spread throughout Europe. The violin was gradually developed over the course of the 16th and 17th centuries: it did not gain its classic outline until around 1550 and a fourth string was not added to the instrument until later.

Originally, the violin family was not regarded as the most prestigious of the bowed stringed instruments. In the Renaissance and Baroque periods, the viol was much more important, and English composers such as Byrd and Purcell composed for consorts of

them. Viols usually had 6 gut strings, were fretted and were positioned and played between the legs, a bit like the modern cello. Bass viola de gambas continued to be popular as a solo instrument into the 18th century. The Bate Collection has a German example from the 19th century along with instruments from the 20th century. There are also viola d'amores on display here. These instruments are not strictly part of the viol family, but have a lot in common with them in terms of tone and construction.

BOWED STRING ACOUSTICS

The violin family of instruments is tuned in fifths; whereas the viol family is tuned in fourths.

Cello and violin by Henry Jay

Jay was working in central London in the mid 18th century. He based the design of his instruments on the successful Italian style.

KEYBOARD INSTRUMENTS

The Collection has a selection of historically important keyboard instruments. These are in the following families: harpsichords (including virginals and spinets), clavichords and pianos.

Keyboard instruments can find their origins in the 3rd century BC with the invention of the hydraulis by Ctesibius of Alexandria. The hydraulis (or water organ) worked by converting the dynamic energy of water into air pressure. The modern church organ is ultimately derived from it. The harpsichord did not emerge until the 14th century AD. The medieval psaltery, which had metal strings held in tension over a soundboard, is often considered its predecessor. Instead of plucking the strings by hand, as on the psaltery, the harpsichord player touches a key, which causes a jack with a quill to pluck the string. A single key might cause a number of strings to be plucked (called a 'choir of strings'). These strings will usually be separated in pitch by one or two octaves and give the harpsichord a richer tone.

An early English harpsichord by Joseph Tisseran is on display in the gallery. It dates from 1700 and is lavishly decorated with scenes drawing their inspiration from Classical Greek art. Its decorative style, in particular the habit of decorating the soundboard of the instrument, draws on traditional Continental harpsichords. Most English harpsichords are much more simply decorated. This can be seen as the inherited design aesthetic from the English reformation when flamboyant design became regarded as counter to new values.

KEYBOARD DYNAMICS

Unlike many other musicians, the keyboard player does not have direct contact with the part of the instrument that produces the noise. It is this crucial difference, which makes keyboards more advanced in terms of construction.

SPINETS

In terms of internal mechanism and construction, spinets are very similar to harpsichords. The main distinguishing feature of a spinet is the angle at which the keyboard is set in relation to the strings. The keyboards of harpsichords are usually at a 90 degree angle to the strings, whereas that of the spinet is at

FOCUS ON...

the William Smith Harpsichord c.1720

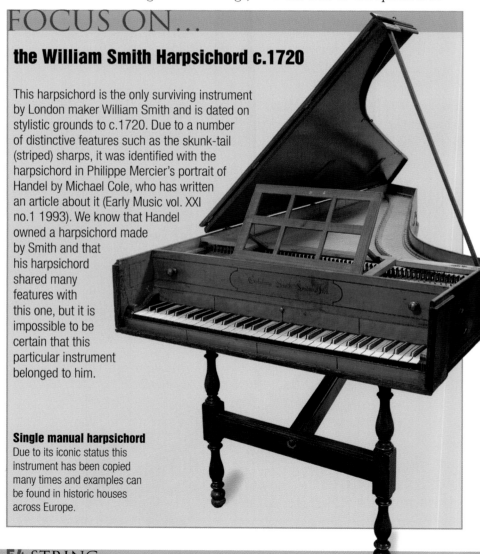

This harpsichord is the only surviving instrument by London maker William Smith and is dated on stylistic grounds to c.1720. Due to a number of distinctive features such as the skunk-tail (striped) sharps, it was identified with the harpsichord in Philippe Mercier's portrait of Handel by Michael Cole, who has written an article about it (Early Music vol. XXI no.1 1993). We know that Handel owned a harpsichord made by Smith and that his harpsichord shared many features with this one, but it is impossible to be certain that this particular instrument belonged to him.

Single manual harpsichord
Due to its iconic status this instrument has been copied many times and examples can be found in historic houses across Europe.

FOCUS ON...

the Piano by Adam Beyer

This is an English single action piano as invented by Johann Zumpe c.1766. It has open-spun covered strings (copper on brass) covering the compass of FF-E. It is thought that many of the strings on this instrument are probably original. It is in an unusually untouched state for a piano of this period. It was reported that it had stood unopened from late 18th century to modern day and when it arrived in the collection a deep layer of dust had accumulated on the interior of the lid. There are three hand levers: damper-lift split between b and middle c', and buff; pedal for right foot lifts the lid to right of keywell as swell; there is also an opening flap the depth of the keywell to its right. It has overdampers with whalebone springs; wooden plate covers dampers. There is a wooden dust cover, straight-grained. These dust covers act as auxiliary sound-boards; their presence or absence makes a considerable difference to the sound. Overall it has a mahogany veneered case with stringing composed of kingwood, box, and ebony. 3 brass hinges to keywell lid, 2 to opening to its right. Trestle stand with square legs; a bar joins right hand legs just off the ground, to which the long, curved wooden pedal is hinged.

approximately 30 degrees. The spinet was designed as a domestic instrument: the soundboard is smaller and the plectra which pluck the strings are arranged closely in pairs which means only one choir of strings can be plucked when a key is pressed. By contrast, on the harpsichord the player could use levers to move the jacks and pluck a different choir of strings, thus varying the instrument's tonality. There are a number of 18th century English spinets on display in the Collection made by London makers such as Harris, Harrison and Hitchcock.

OTHER KEYBOARDS

There are a number of other keyboard instruments in the collection. These include the Ellis harmonical, a type of organ built by Moore & Moore in 1885 to display natural harmonics. The collection also includes a small selection of early square pianos and clavichords.

CLAVICHORDS

The earliest evidence of the development of the clavichord comes from diagrams and illustrations of the 14th century. The action of the clavichord differs significantly from that of the harpsichord: a small brass tangent hits the strings when the player plays the key. This results in a relatively soft sound, which renders the instrument unsuitable for public performance. However, the instrument has much greater expressivity than the harpsichord, as the player has dynamic control. The clavichord was particularly popular in German speaking countries and one of the finest clavichords in the collection was made by the famous German clavichord and harpsichord maker, Hieronymous Albrecht Hass. It was made in 1743 and is magnificently decorated with a scene showing Apollo and the nine Muses. The Collection also includes a Bohemian clavichord that dates to the early 19th century, thought to be made by Deckert. There are other 19th century clavichords by Arnold Dolmetsch and Georg Nikolaus, as well as several modern ones.

SQUARE PIANOS

Bartolomeo Cristofori of Padua, Italy is credited with the invention of the piano sometime before 1700, although the idea did not catch on with other instrument makers until around 1711. The piano-forte drew on the qualities of the harpsichord and the clavichord: it combined the greater expressivity

the Hass Clavichord

This instrument was built in Hamburg in 1743 by Heironymus Albert Hass. It is one of the larger instruments of the type with 5 octaves. It has 4-foot strings which have the effect of brightening the tone of the lowest octave and a half. Hass and his son were considered to be the greatest German clavichord makers, and they created this type of clavichord, for which C. P. E. Bach wrote his famous '*Essay on the True Art of Playing Keyboard Instruments*'. It is a highly decorated instrument in the classical style with allegorical scenes in the cartouche on the inside of the lid.

Late baroque clavichord
One of our most highly-decorated instruments, the cartouche features an alegorical scene with Perseus and Pegasus.

Keys
The convention of colouring natural keys white and accidental keys in another colour is a relatively recent development. Historically keys could be very highly decorated.

integral to the clavichord with the greater amplitude of the harpsichord. In terms of action, the piano was the most like the clavichord: Cristofori developed a system in which a hammer would strike the string, but not remain in contact with it (which would dampen the sound). The piano was initially very expensive and it was therefore not regularly used for public performance until c.1760.

The earliest pianos in the collection date to the end of the 18th century. In this period, the piano was still being developed. Work was focused on making the frame more robust, giving the instrument a more powerful sound and increasing its range. Square pianos were particularly popular throughout Europe and North America as they were reasonably inexpensive and relatively compact. A square piano by the London maker Adam Beyer dated to 1779 has a range of five octaves. Its pedal acts as a swell – giving the player control over the volume.

Purpose of the Bate Collection

The Bate is one of the few collections in Europe that actively encourages the playing of its instruments where reasonably possible. Many of the instruments can be used either for examination or for playing, in order to observe the variations between historical instruments and their modern counterparts. This was the original purpose of the Collection as conceived by Philip Bate, and it has always been a guiding principle for the use of the Collection.

The Collection does have a duty of care for historical objects, which need to be preserved for the enjoyment of future generations. Beyond that, there is a duty to the wider public; the Bate Collection runs educational school visits, concerts, recitals and numerous events for other museum professionals. Nevertheless, its primary function is to serve as a resource for the students and Professors of the Faculty of Music of the University of Oxford.

SERVICES

FRIENDS OF THE BATE COLLECTION

The Friends of the Bate Collection is a charitable association that exists to support the work of the curators and staff. The Friends recieve regular news letters, discount in the Bate shop and reduced prices on tickets for concerts and recitals. There are a regular series of lectures, informal musical introductions and other social events. More importantly the Friends have the unique opportunity of supporting the work of a world-class collection through raising funds for the purchase of new exhibits and through voluntary help at special events and open days.

Levels of membership
- Friend
- Couple
- Overseas Friend
- Student Friend
- Concessions
- Supporter

For current prices visit the website at www.bate.ox.ac.uk

PUBLIC OPENING HOURS

Admission is free

We are open to the publicon weekday afternoons from 2.00–5.00 (apart from block leave at Easter and Christmas). We are also open on Saturday mornings from 10.00–12.00 during the University term time, details of which can be found on the Universty web site.

PUBLICATIONS

The Bate produces its own series of pamphlets and catalogues relating to the collection. These can be purchased in the Bate shop or from our online store.

TECHNICAL DIAGRAMS

The Bate produces technical workshop notes and digital images of many or it's more important instruments. These are available and from the online store. We are continually adding to the list.

CDS AND SOUND SAMPLES

We have been working with a number of hightly-skilled professional musicians making high quality recording of instruments from the Collection. Many of these are now on CD and are available from the shop and the online store.

RESEARCH

Visiting researchers and scholars with a specialist interest in the history and development of musical instruments are welcome to contact us with a view to working with the Collection.

EDUCATION

The Bate runs a series of education visits for schools, family education and tours for life-long learners. Under the programme '*Hands-on Music in Museums*' we explore the major historical periods of the Rennaisance, Baroque, Classical, Romantic and twentieth century through the Bate Bollection instruments. Participants can examine the musical and social development of ensembles, and play musical instruments from the handling collection.

CONTACT

The Bate Collection of Musical Instruments
Faculty of Music
St Aldate's
Oxford
OX1 1DB

Tel: +44 (0) 1865 276139

Email: bate.collection@music.ox.ac.uk
Website: www.bate.ox.ac.uk

index & acknowledgements

The Bate Collection would like to thank Veronica Ford for additional text, Catherine Lieben for proof-reading, Graham Stratford for proof-reading, Graham and Diana Wells for proof-reading, Jonathan Cross and Michael Fleming for additional images, Phillipe Bolton for the Stanesby manuscript on p12, and Gary Newborough for the Higham factory image on p38. Special thanks are due to Gary Ombler for the exquisite photography of the instruments in the collection and Bryn Walls, without whom it would not have happened.